# SPELLING

## RULES and PRACTICE 4

Susan J. Daughtrey M.Ed.

Childs World Education Limited
1995

# CONTENTS

# HOMOPHONES

> A *homophone* is a word which sounds the
> same as another but which has a different
> meaning and may have a different spelling.

Example:

see   and   sea
hair   and   hare
key   and   quay
been   and   bean

**Exercise One:**_____

With the help of a dictionary, put the correct word into the correct space.

ceiling
sealing
He is _____ the _____ with plaster.

principle
principal
The _____ of the school explained the _____ of acceleration.

holy
wholly
I am _____ in agreement with the teaching of the _____ scriptures.

licence
license
I received my driving _____ through the post.
Now I am _____d to drive without learner plates.

practise
practice
Great! There is a football _____ tonight.
Now I can _____ my striking tactics.

manner
manor
The _____ in which she spoke gave the impression she was the Lady of the _____.

cellar
seller
The _____ of coal said it would be all right to put the coal sacks in the _____.

medal
meddle
Please do not _____ with the trophies and _____s.

council
counsel
The _____ official stated that he was prepared to _____ the people's representative.

mettle
metal
He showed a lot of _____ when he volunteered to remove the _____ girder without help.

dual
duel

_____ standards were being practised in the _____.
It resulted unfairly in a draw.

kernel
colonel

The _____-in-chief asked the officer to
explain briefly the _____ of the problem.

canvas
canvass

The parliamentary representative asked if he could _____ under
_____ this year as last year the weather was appalling.

conker
conquer

It is Khaled's ambition to _____ James at _____ s
this autumn.

weather
whether

_____ the _____ be hot, or _____ the _____ be cold
- we'll still go to the seaside!

lesson
lessen

"Please _____ the noise or the _____ cannot begin," Mr. Kerr
told the class.

boarder
border

Sara is a _____ now. She lives at school which is close to the
_____ of the country.

stationary
stationery

The youth remained _____ for a moment watching the _____
from the stall take off into the windy skies!

carat
carrot

"No, boy!" yelled Mr Cowen. "You measure the weight of diamonds in
_____ s, not _____ s. Those are for donkeys!"

bridal
bridle

The _____ procession was led by a magnificent white horse which
had roses attached to its _____.

muscle
mussel

He used all of his _____ s to lift the heavy box of _____ s
onto the fish stall.

## Exercise Two: _____

Find a *homophone* for each of the following words. Write each one on the line next to its partner.
Underneath use the homophone you have found in a sentence of your own so that the meaning of it
is clear from the way you have used it.

key _____

_____

stare _____

_____

tide _____

_____

queue _____

_____

yolk _____
_____

lord _____
_____

hail _____
_____

taught _____
_____

cast _____
_____

pier _____
_____

flare_____
_____

carrot_____
_____

place _____
_____

pair _____
_____

tire_____
_____

piece _____
_____

leak _____
_____

fair_____
_____

Can you think of five words of your own that have the *same sound*, a *different meaning* but the *same spelling*. Indicate in brackets next to your word whether it is a noun (n.), an adverb (adv.), a verb (v.) or an adjective (adj.). Two examples are given.
Examples:

        vault (*n.*) and vault (*v.*)            major (*adj.*) and major (*v. or n.*)

_____

_____

Use two of your words in sentences of your own so the meaning of each word is clear from the way you have used it.

_____

_____

# PREFIXES

---

PREFIX means *to fix to the beginning*.


**A *prefix* is a letter or group of letters that is added
to the *beginning* of a word to make a new word
- to change or extend its meaning.**

---

Many words in the English language come from Latin. Each word can be divided
into a *prefix* and a *root*. The *root* is the basic meaning of the word and remains
'fixed'. When a different *prefix* is added, the meaning of the word is changed slightly
depending upon the meaning of the prefix.

Let us take the root *ject* which means *throw*. By affixing different prefixes (or
groups of letters) to this *root*, we can get several words which sound similar to each
other (because they all have the same *root*) but have a different meaning, depending
upon the definition of the prefix.
Example:

|         |           | Meaning: |
|---------|-----------|----------|
| Root:   | ject      | to throw |
| Prefix: | de        | down, from, away |
| Word:   | deject(ed) | *adj*:miserable, unhappy, in low spirits. |
|         |           |          |
| Root:   | ject      | to throw |
| Prefix: | inter     | among, between |
| Word:   | interject | *verb*: to say something that interrupts someone who is speaking. |
|         |           |          |
| Root:   | ject      | to throw |
| Prefix: | re        | back, again |
| Word:   | reject    | *verb*: you do not accept or agree. *noun*: a product which cannot be used because there is something wrong with it. |

So, by understanding the meaning of the *root* of a word and the different *prefixes*,
your knowledge of the meaning of words is enhanced and compositions and accounts
at school are bound to benefit from your improved use of vocabulary.

Can you compose three sentences using the three words above so that the meaning of each word is
clear from the way you use it?

|            | dejected | interject | reject |
|------------|----------|-----------|--------|

_____

_____

_____

## Exercise Three: _____

Attach the *prefixes* below to the three *root* words given to create new words.

Look up these words in your dictionary and write down the definition of each word you have created. Put *v.* for verb, *n* for noun etc. as indicated in your dictionary so it is clear which meaning you are giving. The first one has been done for you.

**NOTE**: sometimes a word cannot be created. In those cases *NO WORD* has been written in the column for you.

| **PREFIX:** | **ROOT:** | | |
|-------------|-----------|-----------|-----------------|
|             | ject (*throw*) | sist (*stand*) | cede (*yield, move*) |
| de (down from) | _____deject(ed)____ | _____desist_____ | _____no word_____ |
| inter (among, between) | _____ | _____no word_____ | _____ |
| re (back again) | _____ | _____ | _____ |
| pro (forth) | _____ | _____no word_____ | _____no word_____ |
| ab (away from) | _____ | _____no word_____ | _____no word_____ |
| per (through) | ____no word_____ | _____ | _____no word_____ |

Meanings:

_deject(ed):_*adj.* miserable, unhappy, downcast _____
_desist:_*v.*_to stop doing something, to abstain _____

_____

_____

_____

_____

_____

_____

_____

_____

In all these cases the prefix did not change its spelling. However, occasionally the prefix does change its spelling so that the whole word is easier to pronounce. In many cases the effect is to look like doubling. This may help you to remember the spelling.

Example:

Prefix:                                        com (meaning: *with, together*)

Using this prefix we can get such words as:

*com*bine
*com*bat
*com*pile
*com*mit

*Com* would be difficult to say with the root *lide* (meaning: *to clash*) *comlide*, so for ease of pronunciation the *m* in *com* is changed to *l*, and so we have the word *collide* which looks like doubling.

*Com* changes to *cor*    in    *cor*relation
to *con*    in    *con*struct    and    *con*nect
and drops the *m* completely    in    *co*-operate

**Exercise Four:** _____

Down the side of the page is given a list of *prefixes* with meanings. Across the top of the page, *roots* with meanings. With the aid of your dictionary, place the following words into the correct column. Note: Those spellings which have been altered to make the pronunciation easier are marked with an asterisk.

Write the meanings of the words on the lines provided at the bottom of the Exercise.

trajectory*   insist       inject       subtend      conjecture   subject      eject*
transistor    extend       attend*      consist      adjective    exist*       object
                                         intend       contend

| **PREFIX** | **ROOT** ject(*throw*) | sist(*stand*) | tend(*stretch*) |
|---|---|---|---|
| ad (to, towards) | _____ | ___no word___ | _____ |
| sub (below, under) | _____ | ___no word___ | _____ |
| trans (across, beyond) | _____ | _____ | ___no word___ |
| con (with, together) | _____ | _____ | _____ |
| ob (against) | _____ | ___no word___ | ___no word___ |

ex
(out of, outside)          _____    _____    _____

in
(in, into, within)         _____    _____    _____

Meanings:

trajectory        _____

insist            _____

attend            _____

conjecture        _____

eject             _____

extend            _____

consist           _____

adjective         _____

exist             _____

subject           _____

inject            _____

contend           _____

intend            _____

transistor        _____

object            _____

subtend           _____

## Exercise Five: _____

Place into alphabetical order the sixteen words in Exercise Four.

| | | | |
|---|---|---|---|
| 1. _____ | 5. _____ | 9. _____ | 13. _____ |
| 2. _____ | 6. _____ | 10. _____ | 14. _____ |
| 3. _____ | 7. _____ | 11. _____ | 15. _____ |
| 4. _____ | 8. _____ | 12. _____ | 16. _____ |

## Exercise Six: _____

Write another two words from the dictionary which use each of the following *prefixes*. Two words are already given.

ad (*to, towards*): *advance, adverse* _____

con (*with*): *construct, connect* _____

de (*away from*): *de*cline, *de*viate _____

dis (*removal of thing or quality, apart*): *dis*member, *dis*able _____

ex (*out of*): *ex*crete, *ex*clude _____
(**ex* is never followed by *s*: we say *ex*ist, not *exs*ist.)

in (can mean *in* or *not*): Here it means *in*: *in*filtrate, *in*volve_____

Here *in* means *not*: *in*sincere, *in*credible_____

*in* (*not*) in front of *l* becomes *il*: *il*legal, *il*legible _____

*in* in front of *r* becomes *ir*: *ir*regular, *ir*relevant _____

*in* in front of *m*, *p and b* becomes *im*: *im*mature, *im*possible, *im*balance _____

inter (*among, between*): *inter*national, *inter*continental _____

ob (*against*): *ob*ject, *ob*struct_____

*ob* in front of *f* becomes *of*: *of*fend _____

*ob* in front of *p* becomes *op*: *op*pose, *op*ponent _____

per (*through*): *per*vade, *per*ambulate _____

pre (*before*): *pre*set, *pre*select _____

pro (*forward, out*): *pro*ject, *pro*duce _____

re (*back*): *re*ject, *re*treat _____

sub (*below, under*): *sub*marine, *sub*normal_____

*sub* becomes *suc* before *c*: *suc*cour, *suc*cumb_____

*sub* becomes *suf* before *f*: *suf*fice, *suf*fix _____

*sub* becomes *sup* before *p*: *sup*plant, *sup*ply_____

trans (*across, beyond*): *trans*mit, *trans*fer_____

*trans* can also be shortened to *tra*: *tra*duce, *tra*verse_____

ambi (*round, on both sides, both*): *ambi*ent, *ambi*guous _____

ante (*in front of, before*): *ante*natal, *ante*cedent_____

anti (*against, opposing, opposite to*): *anti*social, *anti*thesis_____

## Exercise Seven:_____

Use any of the *prefixes* from the Exercise above with each *ROOT* below to make two more words. One example of each is given.

| | | |
|---|---|---|
| port (*carry*) | *trans*port | _____ |
| mit and mis (*send*) | *sub*mit | _____ |
| pose (*place*) | *im*pose | _____ |
| scrip and scrib (*write*) | *in*scribe | _____ |
| fect (*do*) | *per*fect | _____ |
| tract (*draw, pull*) | *re*tract | _____ |
| spec, spect or spic (*look*) | *in*spect | _____ |

Look up the meaning of any of the words in Exercises Six and Seven about which you are unsure.

Make up three sentences below using as many of these words as possible.

_____

_____

_____

_____

_____

_____

## Exercise Eight: _____

Put the prefixes *ex, con(com), pro* or *per* into the spaces below to make words of two syllables. The number of words possible, is indicated in the brackets next to the *root*. Use a dictionary to help if necessary.

Note that the prefix *ex* is never followed by *s*. Drop the *s* when using the prefix *ex*.

| | |
|---|---|
| _____spire (3) | _____ |
| _____cept (3) | _____ |
| _____tinct (1) | _____ |
| _____pense (1) | _____ |
| _____cite (1) | _____ |
| _____pel (2) | _____ |
| _____clude (2) | _____ |

_____sist (3)              _____

_____fuse (3)             _____

_____duct (2)             _____

_____cede (1)             _____

_____verse (2)            _____

_____pose (2)             _____

_____form (3)             _____

## Exercise Nine: _____

Use the following words in sentences of your own so the meaning of each word is clear from the way you have used it. A dictionary may help.

conspire              concede              profuse              perverse

_____

_____

_____

Not all *prefixes* are derived from a foreign language. Many Anglo-Saxon prefixes exist and their meaning is quite clear. Prefixes such as:

in     out     fore     for     be     to     up     over     under

Complete the following Exercise using some of these *prefixes*.

## Exercise Ten: _____

Put the *prefix* into the gap in each word given, then rewrite the word on the line provided, saying aloud each letter as you do so. Study the letter patterns and syllables of each word and when you are ready, cover and try to write it from memory.

in (meaning *in, into*):

___board    _____  _____         ___put    _____  _____

___set      _____  _____         ___lay    _____  _____

___flow     _____  _____         ___land   _____  _____

___road     _____  _____         ___shore  _____  _____

___going    _____  _____         ___let    _____  _____

___side     _____  _____         ___most   _____  _____

___sole     _____  _____         ___take   _____  _____

What is an *inlet*? _____

_____

If you make an *inroad*, what do you do?_____

_____

What would you describe as *inmost*?_____

_____

What is likely to be *inboard*? _____

_____


**Exercise Eleven:** _____

As you did in the Exercise above, put the *prefix* into the gap in each word below. Rewrite the word on the line provided, saying aloud each letter as you do so. Study the word, and when you are ready, cover and try to rewrite it from memory.

Out (meaning *out of, beyond, away from, external*):

| __break | _____ | _____ | __flow | _____ | _____ |
| __lying | _____ | _____ | __post | _____ | _____ |
| __landish | _____ | _____ | __going | _____ | _____ |
| __moded | _____ | _____ | __skirts | _____ | _____ |
| __cast | _____ | _____ | __burst | _____ | _____ |

There are two parts to this question:
a. What is the meaning of each of the following adjectives?
b. Which noun might each adjective be used to describe?

    outlying         outspoken         outlandish         outmoded

_____

_____

_____

_____


**Exercise Twelve:** _____

As you did in the Exercise above, put the *prefix* into the gap in each word below. Rewrite the word on the line provided, saying aloud each letter as you do so. Study the word, and when you are ready, cover and try to rewrite it from memory.

Fore (meaning *before*, *the front part*):

____father      _____  _____      ____sight      _____  _____

____ground      _____  _____      ____head       _____  _____

____court       _____  _____      ____man        _____  _____

What is the difference between *insight* and *foresight*? Explain fully.

_____

_____

_____

What is a *foreman*?

_____

_____

Under (meaning *beneath, below*):

____coat        _____  _____      ____foot       _____  _____

____ground      _____  _____      ____pin        _____  _____

____study       _____  _____      ____pass       _____  _____

____mine        _____  _____      ____dog        _____  _____

____hand        _____  _____      ____growth     _____  _____

What would you describe as *underhand*?

_____

_____

Who is an *understudy*?

_____

_____

Who is an *underdog*?

_____

_____

What do you do if you *undermine* something?

_____

_____

**Exercise Thirteen:** _____

As you did in the Exercise above, put the *prefix* into the gap in each word below. Rewrite the word on the line provided, saying aloud each letter as you do so. Study the word, and when you are ready, cover and try to rewrite it from memory.

For (meaning: *away, off, prohibit, neglect*)

| ____sake | _____ | _____ | ____bear | _____ | _____ |
|----------|------------|------------|----------|------------|------------|
| ____bid  | _____ | _____ | ____go   | _____ | _____ |
| ____give | _____ | _____ | ____get  | _____ | _____ |

Use the following words in sentences of your own so the meaning of each word is clear from the way you have used it. A dictionary may help.

forgo            forbear            forbid            forsake

_____

_____

_____

A (meaning: *on, in, to*)

| ___float | _____ | _____ | ___board  | _____ | _____ |
|----------|-----------|-----------|-----------|-----------|-----------|
| ___blaze | _____ | _____ | ___ground | _____ | _____ |
| ___light | _____ | _____ | ___shore  | _____ | _____ |

Note these *a* words in Exercise Fourteen with double consonants:

**Exercise Fourteen:** _____

Read each word carefully studying the letter patterns. Copy, saying each letter as you write it. Now rewrite dividing each word into its syllables.

| accomplish | _____ | _____ | account    | _____ | _____ |
|------------|------------|-----------|------------|------------|-----------|
| accurate   | _____ | _____ | afford     | _____ | _____ |
| affect     | _____ | _____ | aggression | _____ | _____ |
| allowance  | _____ | _____ | ammunition | _____ | _____ |
| annex      | _____ | _____ | annihilate | _____ | _____ |

| approach | _____ _____ | appoint | _____ _____ |
| applaud | _____ _____ | arrest | _____ _____ |
| assembly | _____ _____ | assume | _____ _____ |
| attempt | _____ _____ | attract | _____ _____ |
| attend | _____ _____ | apply | _____ _____ |

# NEGATIVE PREFIXES

**The most common prefixes are those which indicate a *negative*. They change the meaning of a word to its opposite.**

The main negative prefix is *un*. Placed in front of a **verb** we have such words as:

> *un*do          *un*lock          *un*fasten          *un*tie

In front of an **adjective**:

> *un*able          *un*happy          *un*successful

In front of an **adverb**:

> *un*wisely          *un*friendly          *un*fortunately          *un*justly

Other **negative prefixes** include:

> **mis** (*badly, wrongly*)
> **in** (*not*) - in front of *m*, *p* and *b* becomes *im*
>           in front of *l* becomes *il*
>           in front of *r* becomes *ir*
> **dis** (*reverse, not, remove or release*)

## Exercise Fifteen: _____

Using *un, mis, in, im, il, ir* and *dis* put the correct *negative prefix* in front of the following words. Copy, saying each letter aloud. Study the letter patterns, and when you are ready, cover each word and try to write it from memory.

| possible | _____ _____ | mature | _____ _____ |
| healthy | _____ _____ | perfect | _____ _____ |
| decent | _____ _____ | proportionate | _____ _____ |
| certain | _____ _____ | legal | _____ _____ |

| approve | _____ _____ | fortunate | _____ _____ |
| visible | _____ _____ | trust | _____ _____ |
| fasten | _____ _____ | honest | _____ _____ |
| appropriate | _____ _____ | finished | _____ _____ |
| audible | _____ _____ | passable | _____ _____ |
| true | _____ _____ | sufficient | _____ _____ |
| treat | _____ _____ | print | _____ _____ |
| regular | _____ _____ | polite | _____ _____ |
| mobilize | _____ _____ | important | _____ _____ |
| real | _____ _____ | complete | _____ _____ |
| accessible | _____ _____ | conscious | _____ _____ |
| logical | _____ _____ | licit | _____ _____ |
| proper | _____ _____ | credible | _____ _____ |
| behaviour | _____ _____ | reasonable | _____ _____ |
| believable | _____ _____ | precise | _____ _____ |

Use each of the following words in a sentence of your own so that the meaning of the word is clear from the way you have used it. A dictionary may help.

illegal          inappropriate          inaudible          immobile

_____

_____

_____

_____

## Exercise Sixteen: _____

Many of the words in the following sentences have the wrong *prefixes*. Identify those words, correct and rewrite each sentence underneath with all the words correctly spelt. (There are 20 deliberate mistakes.)

1. Misfortunately he disheard the instructions and disfastened his seatbelt just as the aircraft began to taxi along the runway.

_____

_____

2. There is unsufficient evidence to accuse the thief of unlegal dealings.

_____

_____

3. He is unhonest, intrustworthy, unpolite and uncredible. He is altogether a misreputable character and one I do not wish to know.

_____

_____

4. He is disable to answer your question because he is discertain of the facts.

_____

_____

5. The painting is misfinished because there is unsufficient paint and my brushes are unperfect.

_____

_____

6. The car was dismobilized: unpossible to start. The condition of the non-passable track which was in disperfect condition after the downpour was to blame. His journey was uncomplete. Just how was he to get home, he wondered?

_____

_____

# THE *ie* AND *ei* SPELLINGS

### *i* before *e* or *e* before *i*?

---

As a general rule:
**Use *i* before *e* except after *c*,
or when *ei* says *a* as in *neighbour* and *weigh*.**

---

# THE *ie* SPELLING

**Use *ie* for a long *i* sound.**

**1. We have already seen that *ie* can make a long *i* sound at the end of a word. (See Book One of this Series.)**
Example:

tie

die

pie

2. **When a suffix beginning with *e* is added to a word ending in *y* which is preceded by a consonant, change the *y* to an *i* and add the suffix. This will give an *ie* spelling.**
Example:

supply + er = suppl*ie*r
apply + ed = appl*ie*d
reply + ed = repl*ie*d

but note:          reply + ing = replying

3. **This rule also applies to forming the plural of a word which ends in *y*, or the third person singular of a verb ending in *y*.**
Example:

one spy, two sp*ie*s
I spy, he sp*ie*s
one fly, two fl*ie*s
I fly, he fl*ie*s

**All these *ie* spellings make a long *i* sound.**

4. ***ie* can also make a long *e* or *ear* sound. In all cases there is no *c* preceding the sound.**
Example:

ach*ie*ve
rel*ie*f
bel*ie*ve
f*ie*rcely
cash*ie*r

Exceptions include: friend (a *short e* sound).

## PRACTICE : THE *ie* SPELLING

---

1. *ie* says long *i* at the end of a word.
2. An *ie* spelling is created when the *y* at the end of a word is changed to an *i* before a suffix beginning with *e* is added. This may be at the end of a noun, at the end of a verb in the third person singular or when the plural of a word is being formed.
3. *ie* can also makes a long *e* or *ear* sound, when this spelling is not preceded by a *c*.

---

**Exercise Seventeen:** _____

Say each of the following words aloud and listen carefully to the sound of the *ie* spelling. Then, sort these words into the correct group depending on whether the *ie* spelling is saying long *i* (group 1), long *e* (group 2) or *ear* (group 3). Put *1, 2* or *3* in the brackets alongside the word according to the Rule demonstrated. Copy each word carefully on the line provided.

| | | | | | |
|---|---|---|---|---|---|
| shield | (___) | _____ | harrier | (___) | _____ |
| supplier | (___) | _____ | mischief | (___) | _____ |
| fierce | (___) | _____ | unties | (___) | _____ |
| priest | (___) | _____ | farrier | (___) | _____ |
| cashier | (___) | _____ | besiege | (___) | _____ |
| pierce | (___) | _____ | magnifies | (___) | _____ |
| defied | (___) | _____ | diesel | (___) | _____ |
| niece | (___) | _____ | yield | (___) | _____ |
| furrier | (___) | _____ | replies | (___) | _____ |
| frieze | (___) | _____ | retrieve | (___) | _____ |

**Exercise Eighteen:** _____

Use each of the following words in sentences of your own so that the meaning of each word is clear from the way you have used it. A dictionary may help.

      frieze             harrier             farrier             furrier

_____

_____

_____

# THE *ei* SPELLING

*Ei* **makes a long *e* sound.**

**1. Use *ei* instead of *ie* for a long *e* sound when this spelling follows *c*.**
Example:

rece*i*ve

rece*i*pt

dece*i*ve

ce*i*ling

conce*i*t

perce*i*ve

Exceptions include: heifer, their, leisure (a short *e* sound); seize, seizure, protein, either and neither (*ei* saying *long e* in words where there is no *c*).

**2. *Ei* also makes a long *a* sound.**
Example:

n*ei*ghbour
r*ei*ndeer
r*ei*gn
v*ei*n
sl*ei*gh
for*ei*gn
*ei*ght

Exceptions include: eiderdown, height (a long *i* sound); science (a split vowel sound).

*Ti* and *ci* are pronounced *sh*.
In the following words it seems that *i* comes before *e* even though this spelling is preceded by *c*. This spelling pattern, I would suggest, is not an exception to the *ie/ei* Rule but rather is due to the *sh* Rule. *Ti* and *ci* can make a *sh* sound (as in elec*ti*on, electri*ci*an). I suggest that the *i* of the *ie* spelling is part of the *sh* sound spelling, and *e* is the first letter of the suffix. In the case of a *ci* spelling, this causes the *i* to come before the *e* despite *c* preceding the *ie* spelling.

profic*IE*nt suffic*IE*nt defic*IE*nt effic*IE*nt consc*IE*nce anc*IE*nt pat*IE*nt pat*IE*nce

## PRACTICE : THE *ei* SPELLING

**1. *Ei* makes a long *e* sound when it follows *c*.**
**2. *Ei* makes a long *a* sound.**

**Exercise Nineteen:** _____

Fill in each gap with *ei* or *ie*. All the gaps say *ee*. (Use *ei* after c and *ie* when there is no c.) Then copy carefully on the line provided. When you are ready, cover over each spelling and try to write it from memory.

| rec__ve | _____ | _____ | br__f | _____ | _____ |
| sh__ld | _____ | _____ | c__ling | _____ | _____ |
| dec__ve | _____ | _____ | ach__ve | _____ | _____ |
| f__rce | _____ | _____ | conc__t | _____ | _____ |

perc__ve  _____  _____        n___ce     _____  _____

dec__t    _____  _____        rec__ver   _____  _____

d__sel    _____  _____        shr__k     _____  _____

cash__r   _____  _____        retr__ve   _____  _____

bel__f    _____  _____        conc__ve   _____  _____

rel__f    _____  _____        fr__ze     _____  _____


Use each of the following words in sentences of your own so that the meaning of each word is clear from the way you have used it. A dictionary may help.

conceit          perceive          retrieve          frieze

_____

_____

_____

_____   -----

_____

## Exercise Twenty: _____

Revise the long *a* spelling from Book One of this Series. Then, put *ay*, *ai*, *a-e* or *ei* into the following gaps. Each gap says *ay*. Mark the Exercise, copy each word on the line provided, study each word and when you are ready, cover it and try to write it from memory.

tod__     _____  _____        n__gh      _____  _____

tr__n     _____  _____        for__gn    _____  _____

f__gn     _____  _____        f__nt      _____  _____

Mond__    _____  _____        w__gh      _____  _____

sl__gh    _____  _____        f__t__     _____  _____

sl__      _____  _____        n__ghbour  _____  _____

sl__t__   _____  _____        n__l       _____  _____

p__n      _____  _____        __ght      _____  _____

r__gn     _____  _____        sl__n      _____  _____

r__n      _____  _____        afr__d     _____  _____

## Exercise Twenty-One: _____

Use each of the following words in sentences of your own so that the meaning of each word is clear from the way you have used it. A dictionary may help.

        faint              feint              feign             slain

_____

_____

_____

_____

## Exercise Twenty-Two: _____

Here you are given a choice of spellings. Choose the correct spelling to write on the line provided.

1. The queen _____(rained, raned, reigned) for many years.

2. The _____(thief, theef, theif) picked up the _____ (receever, receiver, reciever) as soon as the telephone rang.

3. He could not _____(beleeve, believe, beleive) the boy would _____(deceeve, deceive, decieve) him.

4. The plaster fell off the _____(sealing, ceiling, cieling) and into the _____(naybours, naibours, neighbours) _____ (feeled, field, feild).

5. The _____ (fearce, fierce, feerse)_____(cheef, cheif, chief) let out a _____(weard, weird, wierd) _____(shreek, shriek, shreik) as soon as he saw the enemy.

We are familiar with recognised vowel digraphs. A *vowel digraph* is when two vowels together make only one sound.
Example:

*ai* as in tr*ai*n

*oe* as in t*oe*

*ou* as in s*ou*p

*ie* as in ch*ie*f, t*ie*, f*ie*rce*

These are examples of recognised vowel digraphs, and have been looked at in detail in this Series of Books.

---

**If two vowels together are not a recognised digraph, they are sounded as two separate syllables.**

---

Example:

rad/i/o

fur/i/ous

opin/i/on

sci/ence*

*ie* can be pronounced as a vowel digraph or as two separate syllables.

## Exercise Twenty-Three:_____

The following words each contain two vowels next to each other which are *not* a recognised *vowel digraph*. Say each word aloud listening carefully to the pronunciation of the word. Then separate each word into syllables between the *i* and the vowel that follows it.
Example:                diary            *becomes*            di/ary
Copy each word on the line provided.

| | | | | |
|---|---|---|---|---|
| curious | _____ | _____ | mysterious | _____ _____ |
| onion | _____ | _____ | furious | _____ _____ |
| cordial | _____ | _____ | radio | _____ _____ |
| zodiac | _____ | _____ | alien | _____ _____ |
| audience | _____ | _____ | familiar | _____ _____ |
| million | _____ | _____ | brilliant | _____ _____ |
| opinion | _____ | _____ | aviation | _____ _____ |
| giant | _____ | _____ | experience | _____ _____ |
| diet | _____ | _____ | riot | _____ _____ |
| glorious | _____ | _____ | serious | _____ _____ |
| barrier | _____ | _____ | science | _____ _____ |
| appropriate | _____ | _____ | denial | _____ _____ |
| dial | _____ | _____ | diary | _____ _____ |

## Exercise Twenty-Four:_____

Use each of the following five words in sentences of your own so that the meaning of each word is clear from the way you have used it. A dictionary may help.

cordial          alien          aviation          appropriate          denial

_____

_____

_____

_____

**Exercise Twenty-Five:** _____

Write four of your own words for each of the following vowel combinations.

*ai* and *ia:*

(*ai* for a long *a* sound, *ia* as two separate syllables)

_____

_____

*oi* and *io:*

(*oi* as an *oy* sound, *io* as two separate syllables)

_____

_____

*ei* and *ie:*

(*ei* as a long *e* sound, *ie* as two separate syllables)

_____

_____

## SILENT LETTERS

In English there are many letters in the spelling of words which are not pronounced when the word is spoken. This has not always been so. Once the silent letters were sounded. For instance the *gh* in words such as *night* and *plough* were pronounced with a deep guttural sound by the Anglo-Saxons. The Normans softened this sound until eventually, although left in the spelling of the word, the sound was no longer pronounced, and we are left with only reminders of this in such words as *cough* and *enough* which are pronounced with a soft *f* sound.

Other cultures had their influences upon the English language. Latin for instance gave us words such as major, maximum, minimum, omnibus, proviso and condemn. In Latin the word condemn would have other letters following it (condemno, condemnare) in which case the *n* would be sounded. When the word was introduced into the English language the *n* remained but was no longer sounded. We give it back its sound, however, when we add a suffix such as *ation* in *condemnation*. Here the *n* is pronounced again. Another Latin word which keeps its Latin ending even though it is not pronounced, is *plumber* from the Latin *plumbum* meaning *lead*.

As we have seen it is not at all true to say that the *e* on the end of a word has no function. Indeed it has a profound influence upon the spoken word - it makes the *c* soft in words such as *centre*, a *g* soft, in words such as *gentle* and of course changes the sound of a vowel from a short (saying its *sound*) to a long (saying its *name*) vowel sound - in words such as hope (not hop), pine (not pin), cute (not cut) and pane (not pan). Without an *e* our language would be quite different.

Once *u* and *v* only had one sign. To show in the written word that a *v* was intended and not a *u*, an *e* was attached to the consonant. Hence now, no English word ends in *v* alone - it is always followed by an *e*. In such words as *love*, *give*, *glove* and *have* then, the *e* is not a *silent e* changing the vowel sound, but rather is once again a reminder of the cultural influences which have affected the English language.

Because of all the influences upon the English language and the resultant changes in pronunciation of words over the centuries, at least half the letters of the alphabet appear at some time in the spelling of a word without being pronounced.

Let us list firstly the most common *silent letters* in the written English language-those of which we are more aware than others.

## Exercise Twenty-Six: _____

Copy the following words carefully. Study the letter patterns and syllables, and when you are ready, cover over each word and try to write it from memory. Circle the *silent letter*.

### 1. **Silent *w*:** Commonly found preceding the letter *r*:

wrong _____ _____  write _____ _____

wrinkle _____ _____  wrangle _____ _____

Other words with a silent *w* include:

sword _____ _____  answer _____ _____

who _____ _____  whose _____ _____

### 2. **Silent *k*:** Commonly found in front of *n*:

knit _____ _____  knight _____ _____

knock _____ _____  knuckle _____ _____

### 3. **Silent *g*:** Commonly found in front of the letter *n*:

sign _____ _____  gnaw _____ _____

design _____ _____  gnash _____ _____

reign _____ _____  gnaw _____ _____

### 4. **Silent *b*:** Commonly found after the letter *m* and before the letter *t*:

dumb _____ _____  plumber _____ _____

numb _____ _____  crumb _____ _____

bomb _____ _____  limb _____ _____

debt _____ _____  subtle _____ _____

## 5. **Silent *h*** : Commonly found after the letter *w* and *r*:

where    _____ _____    why    _____ _____

when    _____ _____    whisper    _____ _____

wheel    _____ _____    whether    _____ _____

rhubarb    _____ _____    rhyme    _____ _____

rhombus    _____ _____    rhythm    _____ _____

An *h* is often silent at the beginning of a word:

honest    _____ _____    hour    _____ _____

heir    _____ _____    honour    _____ _____

These words are treated as though they began with a vowel.
The **indefinite article** *an* is used in front of a word beginning with a silent *h*, rather than the **definite article** *a* which we would normally use in front of a consonant. Hence we say *an* hour, *an* honest man, *an* heir to the throne, and not *a* honour, *a* hour which we would do if we recognised the *h* as a consonant. (We do however, say *a* hotel and *a* horse. In these words, the *h* is not *silent*.)

## 6. **Silent *l*** : Commonly found preceding the letters *m*, *k* and *d*:

calm    _____ _____    palm    _____ _____

walk    _____ _____    talk    _____ _____

yolk    _____ _____    could    _____ _____

should    _____ _____    would    _____ _____

To remember the spelling of w/*ould* use the mnemonic:

| o | u | l | d |
|---|---|---|---|
| *oh* | *you* | *lazy* | *dog* |

## 7. **Silent *p*** : Commonly found preceding *s*, *n* or *t*:

pneumonia _____ _____    psalm    _____ _____

pterodactyl _____ _____    psyche    _____ _____

## 8. **Silent *n*** : Commonly found after *m*:

autumn    _____ _____    column    _____ _____

mnemonic    _____ _____    hymn    _____ _____

What is a *mnemonic*?

_____

_____

## Exercise Twenty-Seven:_____

Can you identify the *silent letter* in the following words? Read each word carefully saying aloud the word as you do so. Which letter is there in the written word, which is not pronounced? Copy each word on the line provided. Write the *silent letter* in the brackets alongside the word. Cover and write from memory.

| | | | | | | |
|---|---|---|---|---|---|---|
| climb | (__) _____ _____ | handsome | (__) _____ _____ |
| iron | (__) _____ _____ | autumn | (__) _____ _____ |
| aisle | (__) _____ _____ | yolk | (__) _____ _____ |
| write | (__) _____ _____ | calm | (__) _____ _____ |
| knot | (__) _____ _____ | vehicle | (__) _____ _____ |
| daughter | (__) _____ _____ | gnash | (__) _____ _____ |
| rhyme | (__) _____ _____ | grandfather | (__) _____ _____ |
| parliament | (__) _____ _____ | comb | (__) _____ _____ |
| whistle | (__) _____ _____ | guard | (__) _____ _____ |
| campaign | (__) _____ _____ | crumb | (__) _____ _____ |
| subtle | (__) _____ _____ | doubt | (__) _____ _____ |
| island | (__) _____ _____ | salmon | (__) _____ _____ |
| soften | (__) _____ _____ | muscle | (__) _____ _____ |
| rhinoceros | (__) _____ _____ | yacht | (__) _____ _____ |
| whisper | (__) _____ _____ | receipt | (__) _____ _____ |
| hymn | (__) _____ _____ | bomb | (__) _____ _____ |
| answer | (__) _____ _____ | ghost | (__) _____ _____ |
| could | (__) _____ _____ | honour | (__) _____ _____ |
| talk | (__) _____ _____ | whose | (__) _____ _____ |
| psalm | (__) _____ _____ | listen | (__) _____ _____ |
| hour | (__) _____ _____ | knife | (__) _____ _____ |
| plumber | (__) _____ _____ | sign | (__) _____ _____ |
| wrong | (__) _____ _____ | limb | (__) _____ _____ |

scent      (__) _____ _____      debt      (__) _____ _____

knock      (__) _____ _____      gnome     (__) _____ _____

lamb       (__) _____ _____      hasten    (__) _____ _____

column     (__) _____ _____      could     (__) _____ _____

fasten     (__) _____ _____      design    (__) _____ _____

wrinkle    (__) _____ _____      rustle    (__) _____ _____

## Exercise Twenty-Eight: _____

Can you add the missing *silent letter* to the words below? Each gap should be filled with a letter which is not pronounced. If you need some help, each word appears somewhere in the previous Exercise. Completely rewrite the word on the line provided. Mark this Exercise, study each word and when you are ready, cover and try to write it from memory.

cou__d     _____ _____      has__en    _____ _____

colum__    _____ _____      __not      _____ _____

__rinkle   _____ _____      crum__     _____ _____

de__t      _____ _____      si__n      _____ _____

g__ard     _____ _____      i__land    _____ _____

su__tle    _____ _____      s__ent     _____ _____

__nash     _____ _____      com__      _____ _____

__rong     _____ _____      __nome     _____ _____

desi__n    _____ _____      has__en    _____ _____

clim__     _____ _____      han__some  _____ _____

ca__m      _____ _____      ai__le     _____ _____

ans__er    _____ _____      __nife     _____ _____

plum__er   _____ _____      autum__    _____ _____

__our      _____ _____      r__ubarb   _____ _____

w__isper   _____ _____      g__ost     _____ _____

__onour    _____ _____      desi__n    _____ _____

__rong     _____ _____      lim__      _____ _____

Revision:
Remember *s* is followed by a silent *t* before an *le* ending, and a silent *u* follows a *g* to 'block' the effect of an *e, i,* or *y* making a soft *j* sound.

# THE *f* SOUND

## *Ph* SAYING *f*

| |
|---|
| **Words derived from Greek use *ph* for *f*.** |

**Exercise Twenty-Nine:** _____

Circle the *ph* spelling in the following words then rewrite the word completely on the line provided. Study the letter patterns and the syllables of each word and when you are ready, cover over each word and try to write it from memory.

| | | |
|---|---|---|
| elephant | _____ _____ | physician |
| physical | _____ _____ | physics |
| physicist | _____ _____ | phase |
| phrase | _____ _____ | phantom |
| phonic | _____ _____ | philosophy |
| pharmacist | _____ _____ | phenomenon |
| photograph | _____ _____ | paragraph |
| telegraph | _____ _____ | autograph |
| geography | _____ _____ | graph |
| alphabet | _____ _____ | hyphen |
| triumph | _____ _____ | telephone |
| microphone | _____ _____ | sphere |
| atmosphere | _____ _____ | emphasis(e) |
| nephew | _____ _____ | orphan |
| prophet | _____ _____ | sulphur |
| apostrophe | _____ _____ | catastrophe |

Use a dictionary to find the meaning of the following words:

graph_____

photo _____

auto _____

tele_____

micro _____

geo _____

phone _____

Then, in your own words, explain what is meant by an:

autograph_____

photograph _____

telegraph _____

telephone _____

microphone _____

geography_____

How many more words can you list below that have *graph* as part of the spelling (and the meaning) of the word? Can you find at least three?

_____

_____

_____

## Exercise Thirty: _____

Using a dictionary and the words in Exercise Twenty-Nine to help you, can you find one word with a *ph* spelling which is linked in some way with each of the following? The first one has been done for you.

syllable, word, sentence,                    _____*paragraph*_____

History, English, Science (2 words):         _____and_____

Science: Chemistry, Biology and              _____

globe, ball,                                 _____

monkey, tiger,                               _____

26 letters: 5 vowels, 21 consonants:         _____

aunt, uncle, niece, _____

film, lens, camera, album, _____

exchange, operator, handset, _____

victory, success: _____

to stress, highlight, underline: _____

calamity devastation disaster tragedy: _____

full stop, comma, colon (2 words): _____

emotional, mental, _____

A child who has no parents: _____

Another name for a *chemist*: _____

We use this to make our voice louder: _____

To sign your own signature: _____

A ghost, an unreal vision: _____

Another name for a doctor of medicine: _____

A yellow element which burns in _____
oxygen with a blue flame:

## Exercise Thirty-One: _____

Each of the following words has an *f* sound in it. This *f* sound may be spelt with an *f* or a *ph*. Decide which spelling *looks right* and cross out the incorrect spelling. Mark the Exercise and then copy out each word. Study the letter patterns and syllables of each word, and when you are ready, cover and rewrite from memory. Check in a dictionary the meaning of any word about which you are unsure.

fotograph/
photograph   _____   _____

phenomenon/
fenomenon   _____   _____

forget/
phorget   _____   _____

telefone/
telephone   _____   _____

forest/
phorest   _____   _____

fysics/
physics   _____   _____

inphected/
infected   _____   _____

phorain/
foreign   _____   _____

| | | | |
|---|---|---|---|
| infatuate/<br>inphatuate | _____ _____ | hemisfere/<br>hemisphere | _____ _____ |
| alfabet/<br>alphabet | _____ _____ | triumph/<br>triumf | _____ _____ |
| reference/<br>repherence | _____ _____ | ophishal/<br>official | _____ _____ |
| sulfur/<br>sulphur | _____ _____ | physical/<br>fysical | _____ _____ |
| confess/<br>conphess | _____ _____ | fase/phase | _____ _____ |
| phix/fix | _____ _____ | fist/phist | _____ _____ |

## Exercise Thirty-Two: _____

Using a dictionary, explain fully the meaning of the following:

To be *infatuated* means: _____
_____

The *reference* section of a library is: _____
_____

A *phase* is: _____

# THE *gh* SPELLING

*gh* is a *consonant digraph* which is usually found at the end of a word or is followed by *t*.

**1. *gh* can say *f*.**
Example:

> tou*gh*
> cou*gh*
> rou*gh*

**2. Sometimes *gh* are silent letters and say nothing at all.**
Example:

> ni*gh*t
> ti*gh*t

**However, put with other letters, *gh* creates different sounds.**

**3. *Au* + *gh* can say *or* or *arf*.**
Example:
*or* sound:

> *caught*
> n*aught*y
> h*aught*y

*arf* sound:                                             l*augh*ter
                                                        dr*augh*t

**4. *Ou + gh* can say *or*, *uf*, *ow*, *off*, *o*, *u* and *oo*.**
Example:
*or* sound:                                             th*ough*t
                                                        s*ough*t
                                                        f*ough*t

*uf* sound:                                             t*ough*
                                                        r*ough*
                                                        en*ough*

*ow* sound:                                             pl*ough*
                                                        b*ough*

*off* sound:                                             c*ough*
                                                        tr*ough*

*o* sound:                                               th*ough*
                                                        d*ough*

*u* sound:                                               thor*ough*

*oo* sound:                                              thr*ough*

## PRACTICE : THE *gh* SPELLING

---

**1. *Gh* can say *f*.**
**2. *Gh* is often silent and says nothing at all.**
**3. *Gh* put with *au* can make an *arf* or an *or* sound.**
**4. *Gh* put with *ou* can make an *or*, *uf*, *ow*, *off*, *o*, *u* or *oo* sound.**

---

**Exercise Thirty-Three:** _____

Say these words aloud and listen carefully to the sound the *gh* spelling is making. Then, sort out these words according to the sound the spelling makes. Place each word in the correct column.

sought  slaughter  rough  bough  thorough  wrought  through
laughter  ought  although  plough  trough  borough  drought
fought  daughter  caught  laugh  enough  fraught

| or | arf | uf | ow | off | o | u | oo |
|---|---|---|---|---|---|---|---|
| | | | | | | | |
| | | | | | | | |
| | | | | | | | |
| | | | | | | | |
| | | | | | | | |
| | | | | | | | |
| | | | | | | | |
| | | | | | | | |

Making new words:

Change the *s* in *sought* to b, f, n, wr, br and th.

sought  _____   _____   _____   _____   _____   _____

Using the above words write the correct word next to its meaning below.

nothing  _____   kicked and struggled  _____

used his brains  _____   purchased  _____

fetched  _____   decorated iron  _____

What does *fraught* mean? _____

**Exercise Thirty-Four:** _____

Put the fourteen words with *ou* spellings in Exercise Thirty-Three into alphabetical order.

_____

_____

_____

_____

_____

# RULE SUMMARIES

Here you are asked to do three things:
1. Read through all the Rules that have been identified in this book, one at a time.
2. When you are ready, fill in the missing words in the Rule Summaries below.
3. Explain in your own words what is meant by each Rule, making reference to the examples given.

## HOMOPHONES

Read through the Exercises and notes on **HOMOPHONES** on pages 1 to 3 and when you are ready complete the following Rule Summary without referring to that section.

A HOMOPHONE is a word which _____ the same as another word but which has a _____ meaning and may have a_____ spelling.

Now turn back to page 1 and check your answer.

### KEEPING YOUR OWN RECORD OF THE SPELLING RULES IN THESE BOOKS

To keep a permanent record of the spelling Rules in these books - a record to which you can refer at any time - you need a pack of 5ins x 8ins index cards and an index card box or A5 file. You have already made Thirty-Three Record Cards from Books One, Two and Three. Continue here with Card Thirty-Four.

### CARD THIRTY-FOUR:

Take an index card 5ins x 8ins and copy the definition of a **HOMOPHONE** from the top of page 1 carefully and clearly on the first side of Card Thirty-Four. Spread out your writing so it is not crammed, but is neat and easy to read.

On the reverse side of this Card, explain in your own words what exactly is meant by a **HOMOPHONE** using as many Examples as you feel are of interest, to illustrate your answer.

### CARD THIRTY-FIVE and THIRTY SIX:

Read the notes about a **PREFIX** and the **ROOT** of a word on page 4, and when you are ready, complete the following Rule Summary without reference to that section.

**PREFIX** means ___ _____ ___ _____ _____.
A **PREFIX** is a _____ or group of _____ that is added to the _____ of a word to make a new word - to _____ or _____ its meaning.
The **ROOT** of a word is the basic _____ of the word, and remains '_____'.
When different prefixes are added, the _____ of the word is _____ slightly depending upon the _____ of the prefix.

Now turn back to page 4 to check your answers. Copy the above Rule Summary carefully and accurately onto the first side of Card Thirty-Five.
On the reverse side of Card Thirty-Five and on Card Thirty-Six, complete the following:
List the **PREFIXES** from Exercises 3, 4 and 6 together with their meanings. Give an example to show the use of each **PREFIX** you list.
Make sure you know the meaning of all the words you are recording on your Cards.
Then, by reference to Exercise 7, make a note of any **ROOT** and its meaning which may be useful.

## CARD THIRTY-SEVEN:

Read the notes on **NEGATIVE PREFIXES** on page 14 and when you are ready, complete the following Rule Summary without referring to that section.

The most common prefixes are those which indicate a _____. They change the meaning of a word to ____ _____.
The main **NEGATIVE PREFIX** is ____. Other negative prefixes include ____ which means ____ _____, ___ which means ____, and ____ which means _____, ___, _____ or _____. The prefix *in* changes to ____ before __, __, and __, *il* before ___, and ____ in front of *r*.

Now check your answers by referring to page 14. Copy carefully and accurately the above Rule Summary onto the first side of Card Thirty-Seven.

Onto the reverse of Card Thirty-Seven record those negative words which may be of most benefit to you in everyday usage. Be careful to spell them correctly, and to know the meaning of these words. Many useful negatives are contained in the Answers to Exercise 15.

## CARD THIRTY-EIGHT:

Read the notes and Exercises on **THE *ei* AND *ie* SPELLINGS** on pages 16 to 19.
When you are ready, complete the following Rule Summary without referring to that section.

As a general Rule:
Use ___ before ___ except after ___, or when _____ says ___ as in _____ and _____.

### THE *ie* SPELLING

1. *ie* says _____ ___ at the end of a word.
2. An *ie* spelling is created when the ___ at the _____ of a word is changed to an ___ before a suffix beginning with ___ is added. This may be at the end of a _____, at the end of a verb in the _____ person _____ or when the _____ of a word is being formed.
3. *Ie* can also make a long ___ or ____ sound, when the spelling is not _____ by a *c*.

### THE *ei* SPELLING

1. *Ei* makes a long ___ sound when it follows ___.
2. *Ei* makes a long ___ sound.

Now check your answers by looking back at pages 17 and 19. When you have corrected the above Rule Summaries, copy them carefully and neatly onto the first side of Card Thirty-Eight.

On the reverse of Card Thirty-Eight:
List any particular spelling you find useful, making a note of the Rule to which it belongs.
List the *exceptions* to the Rules, again identifying the Rule to which each is an exception.

## CARD THIRTY-NINE:

Read about vowels which are **NOT A RECOGNISED DIGRAPH** on pages 21 and 22. When you are ready, complete the following Rule Summary without referring to that section.

If two _____ together are not a recognised digraph, they are sounded as ____ _____ _____.

On the reverse of Card Thirty-Nine, answer the following:

1. What is a *recognised digraph*? Explain fully, giving examples to illustrate *five* different recognised vowel digraphs. (Such as *ai*, *oa*, *ue*, *ou* and *ea*.)

2. How is a word pronounced which contains vowels which are **not** a recognised digraph? Make your own notes, giving as many examples as you find interesting, to illustrate your answer. Mention also, that *ie* can be pronounced as a vowel digraph *or* two separate syllables. Give three examples to illustrate this.

## CARD FORTY:

Read through the notes on **SILENT LETTERS** on page 23 and 24. Then onto Card Forty:

1. Discuss what is meant by **SILENT LETTERS**.

2. List from Exercise 26 on pages 24 and 25 the eight most familiar **SILENT LETTERS** and which letter is most commonly found following or preceding each one.

In all cases, give two examples from Exercise 26 to illustrate the spelling you are discussing.

For example, *Silent w* is usually followed by *r*, and is occasionally preceded by *s*. You could give the examples *write*, *wrong*, *answer*, and *sword* to illustrate your answer.

3. For you own record, make a note of any particular word you might find useful and which you may need to look at again to more thoroughly familiarise yourself with its spelling.

4. What is an *indefinite article*? Discuss, giving examples.

5. What is a *mnemonic*? Discuss the spelling of w/*ould* to illustrate this. Do you know any more? If so, make a note of them here.

## CARD FORTY-ONE:

Read through the notes concerning **THE *f* SOUND** on pages 28 to 33 and on the first side of Card Forty-One list the two different spellings of **THE *f* SOUND: *ph* and *gh*.** Then complete the following Rule Summary without referring back to that section.

### THE *gh* SPELLING

1. *Gh* can say ___.

2. *Gh* can say _____ at all.

3. *Gh* put with *au* can say an _____ or an ____ sound.

4. *Gh* put with *ou* can make an ____, ____, ____, _____, ___, ___ or ____ sound.

Turn back to page 32 and correct your answers.

On the reverse of Card Forty-One, under the particular Rule heading, list words which you find useful to record and which you may need to look at again to better familiarise yourself with the spelling. For example, you may find it useful to record the spellings *plough* and *bough*. These would come under the side heading: *Ou + gh* can make an *ow* sound.

## CARD FORTY-TWO:

Make a note of any of the spellings in Book Four which you have found difficult to remember and which you need to look at again. Alongside each spelling make a note of the Rule to which it belongs and a page reference, so you can look it up and read over the Rule again. Try to learn these words.

**Words I have found difficult to remember in Book Four and which I need to look at again:**

| WORD | RULE | PAGE | LEARNT |
|------|------|------|--------|
|  |  |  |  |
|  |  |  |  |
|  |  |  |  |
|  |  |  |  |

# ANSWERS

## Working *down* the Exercises, the Answers are as follows:

### Exercise 1

- sealing
- ceiling
- principal
- principle
- wholly
- holy
- licence (noun)
- license(d) (verb)
- practice (noun)
- practise (verb)
- manner

### Exercise 2

- quay
- stair
- tied
- cue
- yoke
- laud
- hale
- taut
- caste
- peer
- flair
- carat
- plaice
- pear
- tyre
- peace
- leek
- fare

### Exercise 3

*Across* the columns:

- interject
- intercede
- reject
- resist
- recede
- project
- abject
- persist

### Exercise 4

*Across* the columns:

- adjective
- attend
- subject
- subtend
- trajectory
- transistor
- conjecture
- consist
- contend
- object
- eject
- exist
- extend
- inject
- insist
- intend

### Exercise 5

- adjective
- attend
- conjecture
- consist
- contend
- eject
- exist
- extend
- inject
- insist

### Exercise 8

- expire
- conspire
- perspire
- except
- concept
- percept
- extinct
- expense
- excite
- expel
- propel
- exclude
- conclude

- exist
- consist
- persist
- confuse
- perfuse
- profuse
- conduct
- product
- concede
- converse
- perverse
- expose
- propose
- conform
- perform
- pro-form
- object
- subject
- subtend
- trajectory
- transistor

### Exercise 15

- impossible
- unhealthy
- indecent
- uncertain
- disapprove
- invisible
- unfasten
- inappropriate
- inaudible
- untrue
- mistreat
- irregular
- immobilize
- unreal

### Exercise 16

1. unfortunately
   misheard unfastened
2. insufficient illegal
3. dishonest
   untrustworthy impolite
   incredible disreputable

- inaccessible
- illogical
- improper
- misbehaviour
- unbelievable
- immature
- imperfect
- disproportionate
- illegal
- unfortunate
- mistrust/distrust
- dishonest
- unfinished
- impassable
- insufficient
- misprint
- impolite
- unimportant
- incomplete
- unconscious
- illicit
- incredible
- unreasonable
- imprecise

### Exercise 17

- 2
- 1
- 3
- 2
- 3
- 3
- 1
- 2
- 3
- 2
- 3
- 2
- 1
- 3
- 2
- 1
- 2
- 2

### Exercise 19

- receive
- shield
- deceive
- fierce
- perceive
- deceit
- diesel
- cashier
- belief
- relief
- brief
- ceiling
- achieve
- conceit
- niece
- receiver
- shriek
- retrieve
- conceive
- frieze

4. unable uncertain
5. unfinished
   insufficient imperfect
6. immobilised
   impossible impassable
   imperfect incomplete

### Exercise 20

- today
- train
- feign
- Monday
- sleigh
- slay
- slate
- pain
- reign

- lesson
- boarder
- border
- stationary
- stationery
- carat(s)
- carrot(s)
- bridal
- bridle
- muscle(s)
- mussel(s)

- manor
- seller
- cellar
- meddle
- medal(s)
- council (noun)
- counsel (verb)
- mettle
- metal
- dual
- duel
- colonel
- kernel
- canvass
- canvas
- conquer
- conker(s)
- whether weather
- whether weather
- lessen

rain
neigh
foreign
faint or feint
weigh
fate
neighbourhood
nail
eight
slain
afraid

ra di o
a li en
fam ii i ar
bril li ant
a vi a tion
ex pe ri ence
ri ot
se ri ous
sci ence
de ni al
di ary

**Exercise 22**

1. reigned
2. thief receiver
3. believe deceive
4. ceiling neighbours
field
5. fierce chief weird
shriek

**Exercise 23**

cu ri ous
on i on
cor di al
zo di ac
au di ance
mil li on
o pin i on
gi ant
di et
glor i ous
bar ri er
ap pro pri ate
di al
mys te ri ous
fu ri ous

**Exercise 27**

| | |
|---|---|
| k | g |
| b | t |
| n | l |
| t | g |
| w | t |
| b | d |
| r | n |
| s | l |
| w | l |
| k | h |
| gh | g |
| h | d |
| a | b |
| h and t | u |
| g | b |
| n | b |
| h | p |
| h | n |
| w | h |
| l | h |
| l | h |
| | ch |
| t | c |
| s | l |
| h | ch |
| g | g |
| p and l | t |
| h | t |
| h | k |
| w | g |
| c | b |

**Exercise 28**

could
column
wrinkle
debt
guard
subtle
gnash
wrong
design
climb
calm
answer
plumber
orphan
pharmacist
hour
whisper
microphone
autograph
honour
wrong
hasten
knot
crumb
sign
island
scent
comb
gnome
hasten
handsome
aisle
knife
autumn

rhubarb
ghost
design
limb

**Exercise 30**

philosophy/geography
physics
sphere
elephant
alphabet
nephew
photograph
telephone
triumph
emphasise
catastrophe
apostrophe/hyphen
physical
fought
daughter
phantom
physician
sulphur

fix
forest
physics
infected
foreign
hemisphere
triumph
official
physical
phase
fist

**Exercise 31**

photograph
phenomenon
forget
telephone
infatuate
alphabet
reference
sulphur
confess

**Exercise 33**

or sound:
sought
caught
fraught
ought
fought
enough
rough
drought
bough
plough
rough
sought
thorough
through
trough
wrought

u sound:
borough
thorough
oo sound:

**Exercise 34**

although
borough
bough
drought
rough
ought
fought
enough
through
trough
wrought

ow sound:
bough
plough

arf sound:
laughter
laugh

uf sound:
rough
enough
drought

off sound:
drought
trough

oo sound:
through

although
nought
thought
brought
bought
wrought